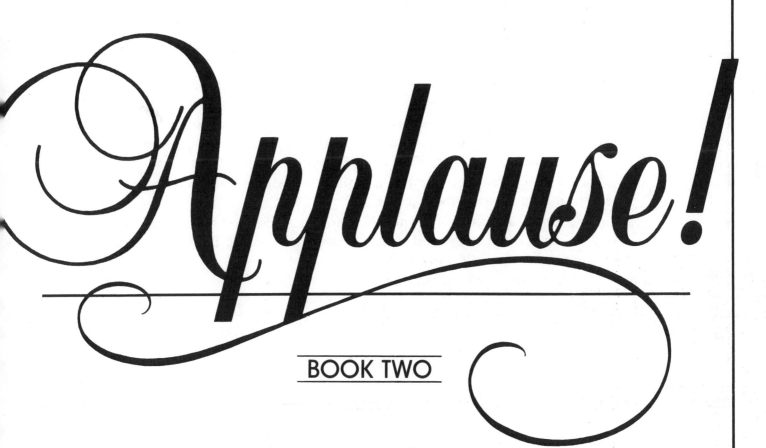

BOOK TWO

Selected and Edited by
Lynn Freeman Olson

Foreword

The piano is center stage, and listeners from every walk of life thrill to the sounds of piano brilliance.

Over the years, emerging pianists have come to recognize certain pieces as inevitable crowd pleasers. These are the pieces that ''sell a recital'' and turn a flattering spotlight on technical ability. While students of piano need to conquer a full spectrum of styles and musical demands in their pianistic lives, each one can make frequent good use of those works that help showcase facility, drive, power, and pure flash.

These two collections contain just such pieces—tried and true for their ability to capture attention and win the applause.

The pieces in each book are arranged in approximate historical order. You will find varying lengths because we wished to include some short encores. Book One material is less advanced than that in Book Two.

Enjoy the music—and the applause!

Lynn Freeman Olson

Note: These collections have been growing for forty years! Like so many pianists, I played any number of ''crowd pleasers'' as a young student, so the first source of these books is my own past—and inspiring teachers. Throughout my professional years as a teacher and itinerant clinician, so many colleagues and mentors have contributed to these books as well! The list could be very long, but I must mention my gratitude to David Caudle, Frances Clark, Erma Coleman, Charlene Cox, Cleo Munden Hiner, Juanita Hubbard, Frances and Edwin Key, Marguerite Miller, Hania Poliakoff, and Carrie Warrick. My thanks also to Iris and Morty Manus at Alfred Publishing who have been so encouraging about this project from the moment the idea arrived.

L.F.O.

Contents

A CD (#4052) recording of the selections contained
in *Applause!* Book Two is available separately.
They are beautifully played by Valery Lloyd-Watts.

AIR AND VARIATIONS
from Suite No. 5
"THE HARMONIOUS BLACKSMITH"

George Frideric Handel

[Moderato]

6

Var. 4

*The B and A were probably intended to be played an octave lower (with the left hand) the second time, to lead more logically into Variation 4.

Var. 5

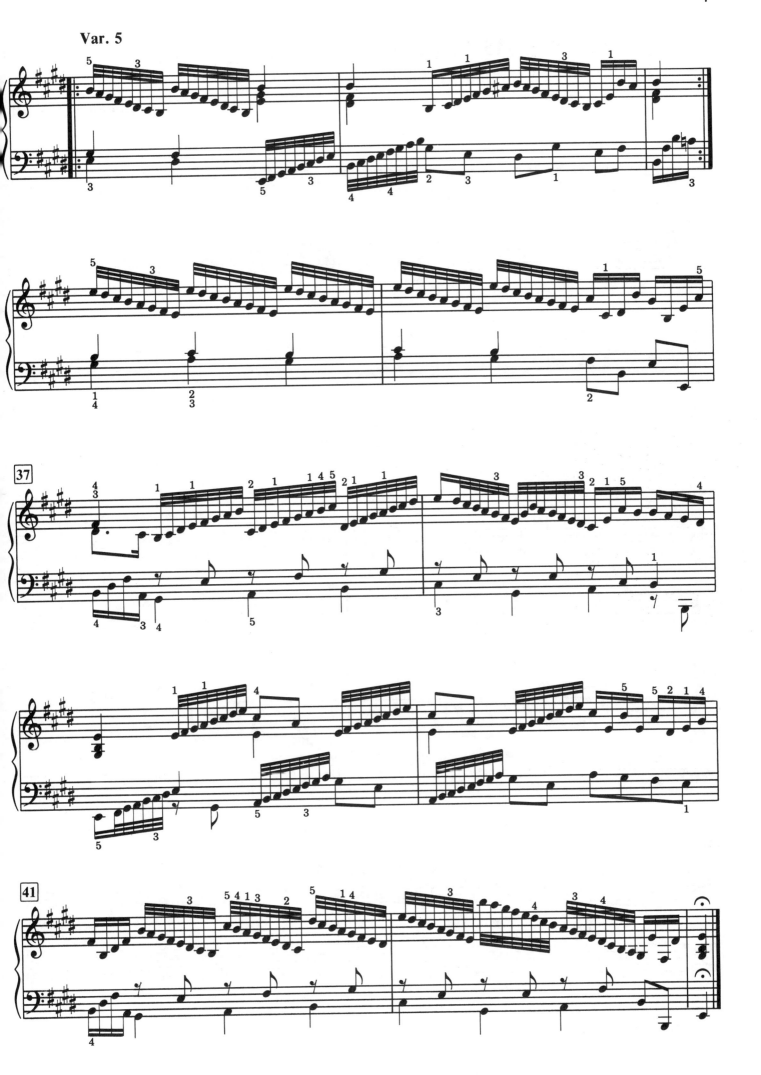

SONATA IN G MAJOR

from *30 Essercizi,* 1738

Domenico Scarlatti

TOCCATA
from Sonata in A

Pietro Domenico Paradisi

* We avoid the excessive editing often associated with this work. Some dynamic suggestions appear; further nuances will be added by each performer. A semi-detached touch may be appropriate for the eighth notes.

14

PRAELUDIUM IN E MINOR

Felix Mendelssohn-Bartholdy

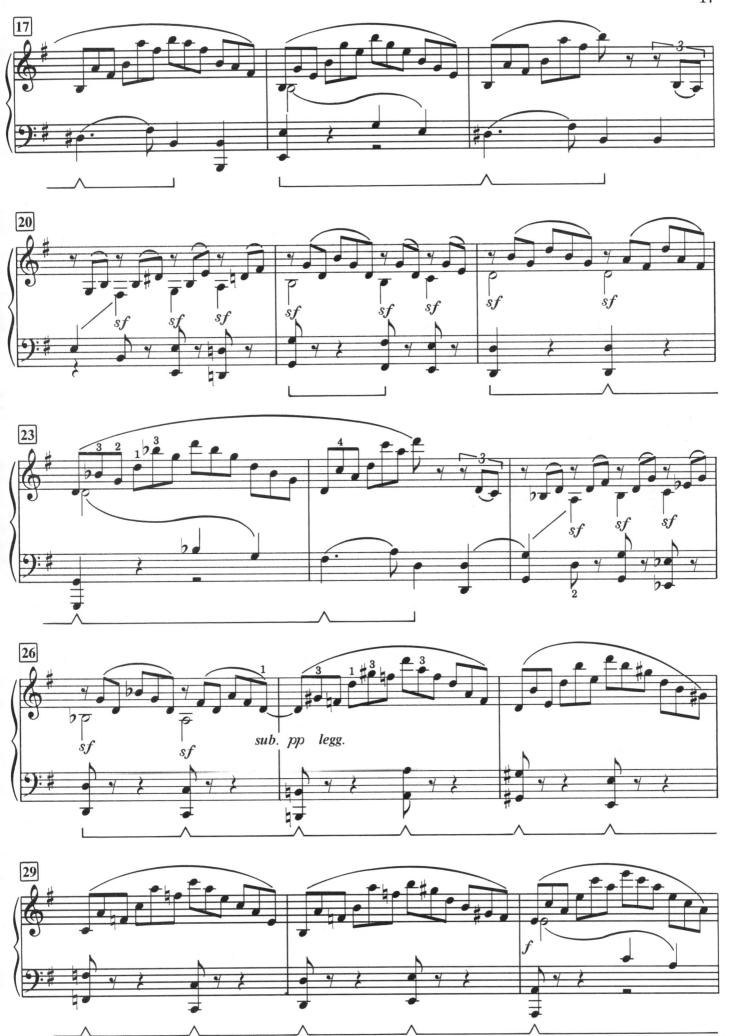

SCHERZO

Felix Mendelssohn-Bartholdy
Op. 16, No. 2

*Often, pedal is used with little clearing from here to the end.
  We suggest occasional half-pedal clearing.

ETUDE IN C MAJOR

Stephen Heller
Op. 46, No. 24

Allegro con brio

WARRIOR'S SONG

Stephen Heller
Op. 45, No. 15

30

WEDDING DAY AT TROLDHAUGEN

Edvard Grieg
Op. 65, No. 6

* For smaller hands, one common solution is to omit the notes shown in parentheses.

HOPAK

Modest Mussorgsky

Allegretto scherzando

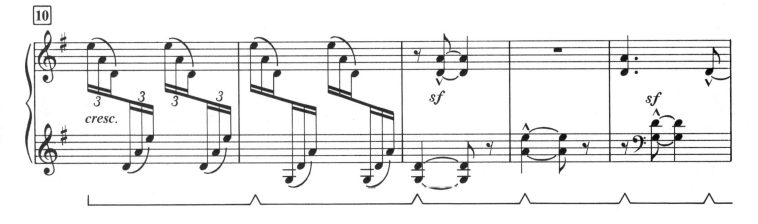

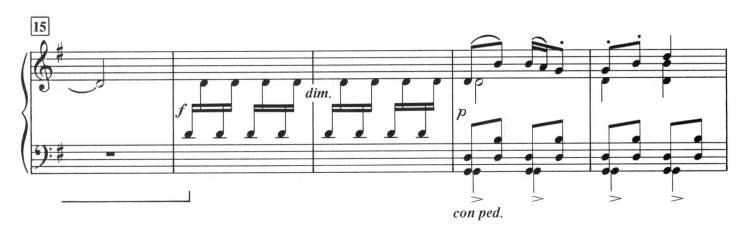

SCHERZINO

Moritz Moszkowsky
Op. 18, No. 2

* Light staccato, both hands throughout, unless marked otherwise.

ROMANCE

Jean Sibelius
Op. 24, No. 9

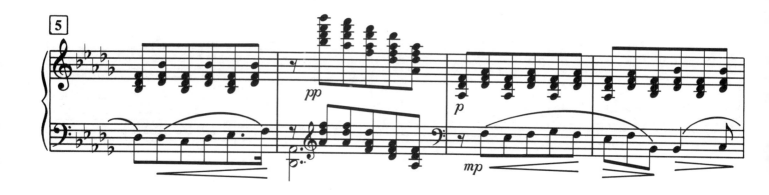

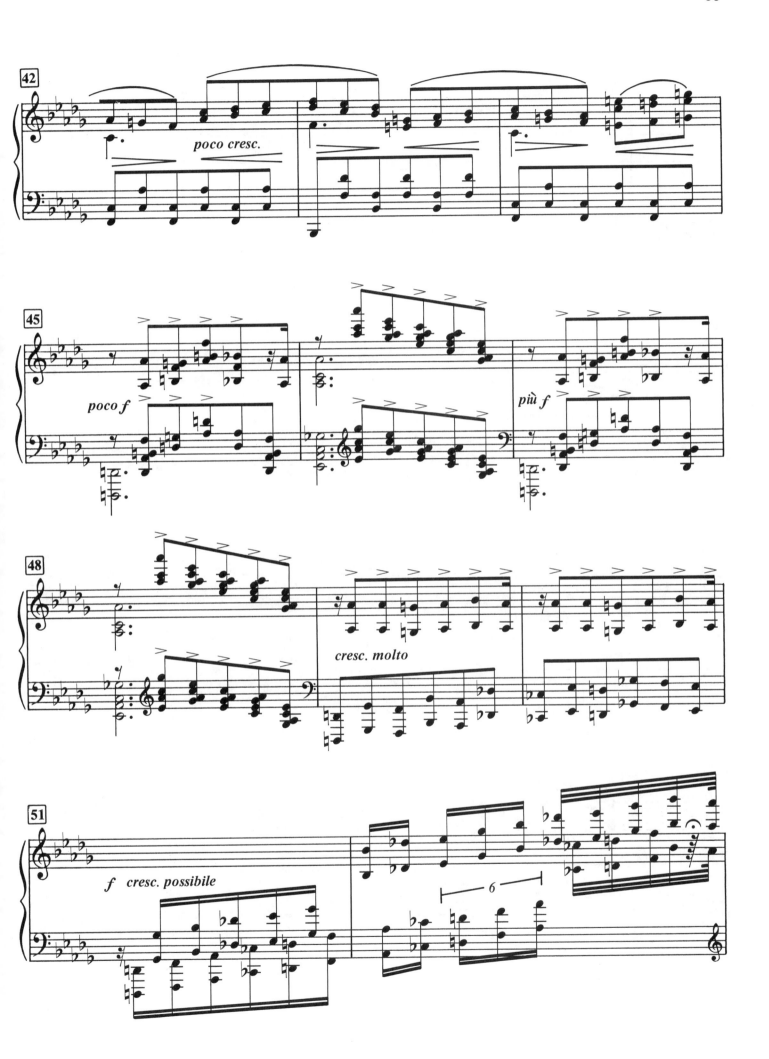

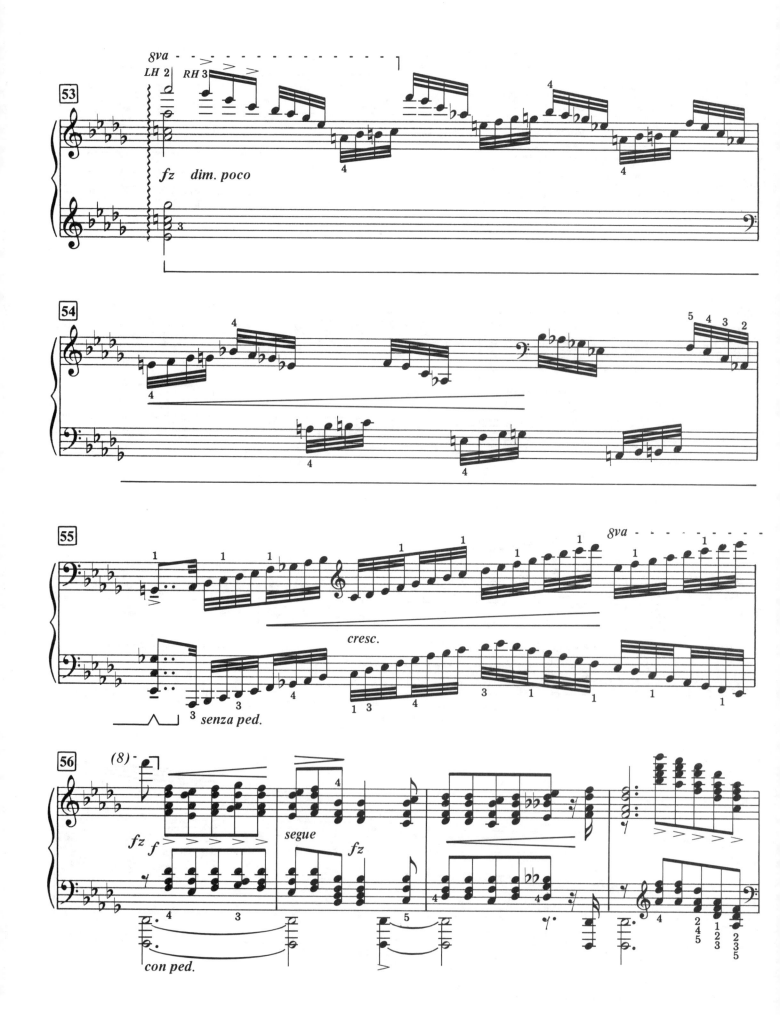

HUNGARIAN

Edward MacDowell
Op. 39, No. 12

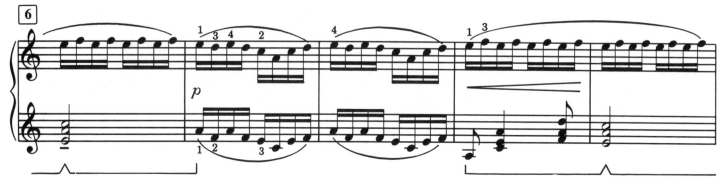

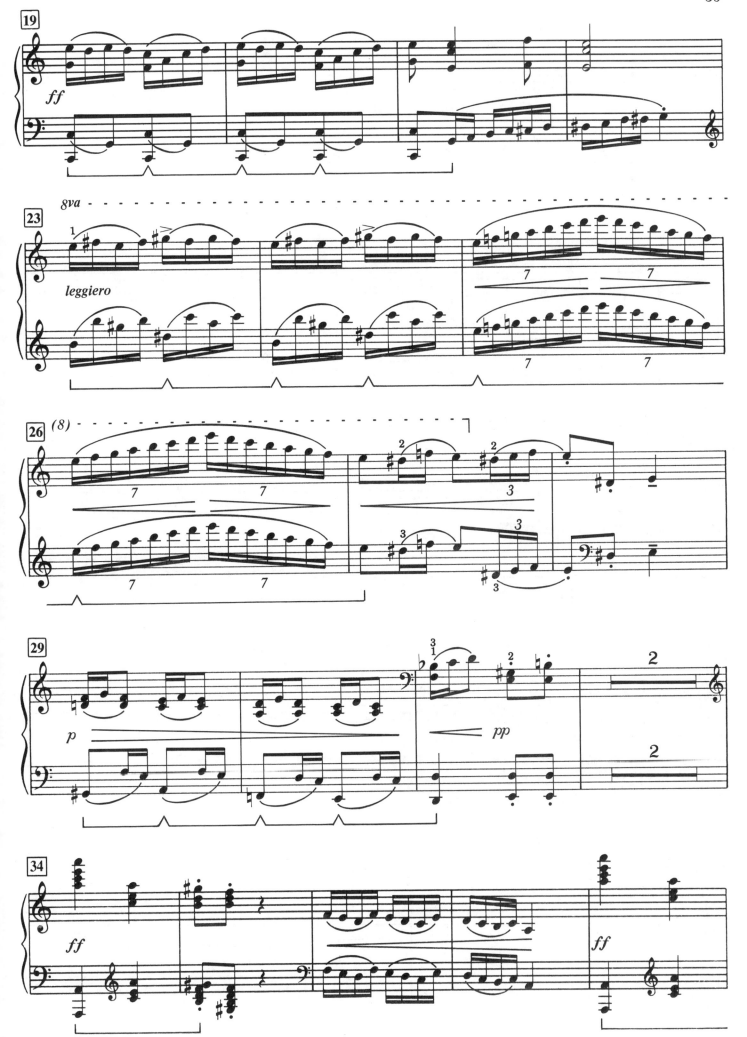

60

ALLA TARANTELLA

Edward MacDowell
Op. 39, No. 2

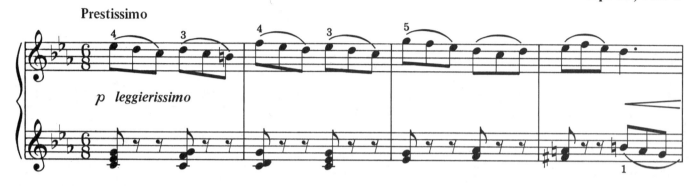

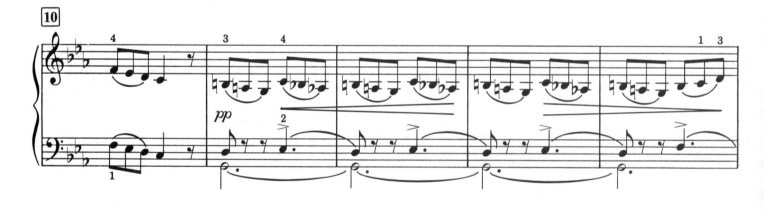

TARANTELLA

Albert Pieczonka

74

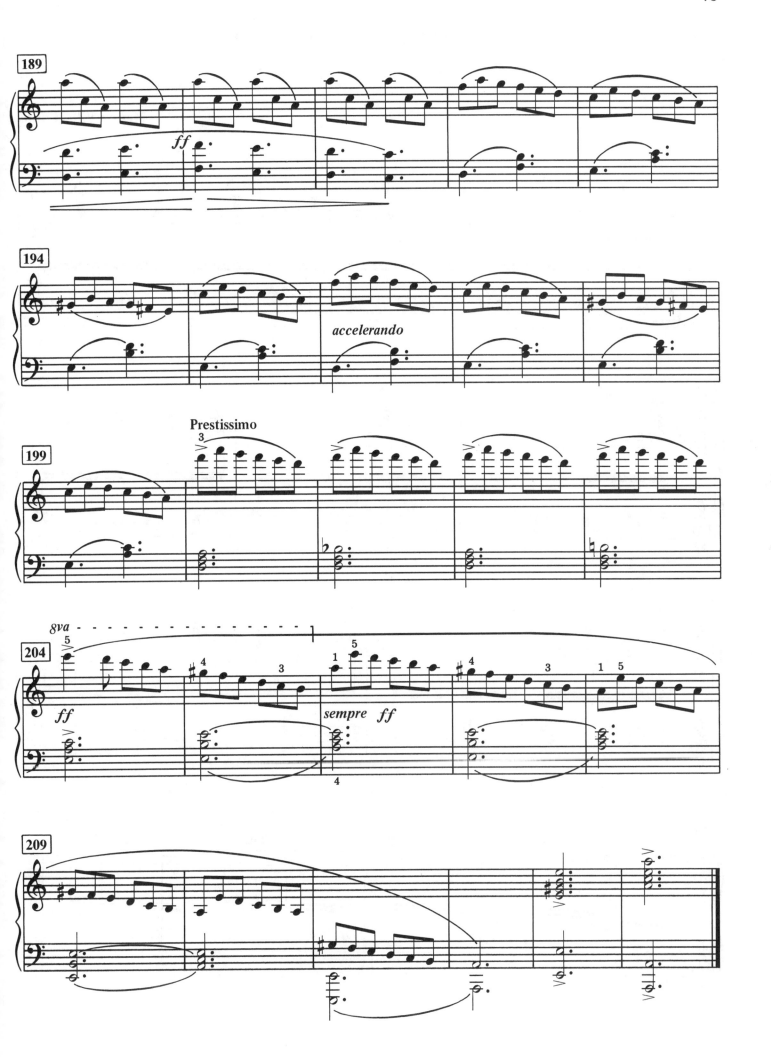

O POLICHINELO
from Prole do Bêbê, No. 1

Heitor Villa-Lobos

* Pedal is often used lightly in these passages.

il canto ben distinto

*When this piece is performed as a solo rather than as part of the cycle, it is usually
played as follows: play through Measure 61, return to Measure 12, then play again
from Measure 12 to the end; finally add a glissando at the end.